The *Colors* of Christmas

Martha Nelson Phifer
Illustrated by Judy I. Roberts

Herald
Press

Scottdale, Pennsylvania
Waterloo, Ontario

Library of Congress Cataloging-in-Publication Data
Phifer, Martha Nelson, 1935-
      The colors of Christmas / Martha Nelson Phifer ; illustrated by Judy I. Roberts
            p. cm.
      Summary: Green hills, white sheep, purple robed kings on brown camels, and other colorful
objects portray the story of the birth of Christ in the manger in Bethlehem.
      ISBN 0-8361-9029-7 (alk. paper)
      1. Jesus Christ—Nativity—Juvenile fiction. [1. Jesus Christ—Nativity—Fiction. 2. Christmas—Fiction.
3. Color—Fiction. 4. Stories in rhyme.]
I. Roberts, Judy I., 1957- ill.
II. Title.
PZ8.3.P54Co 1995
[E]—dc20

95-34875

The paper used in this publication is recycled and meets the minimum requirements of American National Standard
for Information Sciences—Permanence of Paper for Printed Library Materials, ANSI Z39.48-1984.

THE COLORS OF CHRISTMAS
Copyright © 1995 by Herald Press, Scottdale, Pa. 15683
      Released simultaneously in Canada by Herald Press,
      Waterloo, Ont. N2L 6H7. All rights reserved
Library of Congress Catalog Card Number: 95-34875
International Standard Book Number: 0-8361-9029-7
Printed in the United States of America
Book design by Paula M. Johnson

07 06 05 04 03 02 01 99 98 97 10 9 8 7 6 5 4 3 2

To Craig, Lynne, Nathan, and Scott,
and families everywhere,
who bring joy to every season.
—MNP

To Sharon,
the best friend a sister can have,
and to Althea,
who is full of encouragement
—JR

*T*HE COLORS OF CHRISTMAS bring gladness and light

To the silence and still of a Bethlehem night.

*G*REEN are the hills where the shepherds go
To watch while their sheep graze to and fro.

*W*HITE are the sheep as they wander the hill
On a winter's night so cold and still.

ED is the fire that glows on the hill
And warms the shepherds against the chill.

*B*LACK is the night till the angels sing,
Bringing good news of the birth of a king.

*Y*ELLOW is the hay in the holy crèche,
Making a bed that is soft and fresh.

B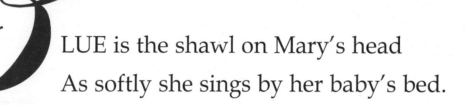LUE is the shawl on Mary's head
As softly she sings by her baby's bed.

ORANGE is the robe Joseph wears this night
As he watches over the holy site.

GRAY is the donkey greeting shepherds and sheep
Come to see baby Jesus fast asleep.

*S*ILVER is the light of the Bethlehem star
Guiding the wise men from afar.

$\mathcal{B}$ROWN are the camels with wise men astride

As they travel to Bethlehem, a very long ride.

*P*URPLE is the color the three kings wear;

Frankincense, gold, and myrrh are the gifts they bear.

*G*OLD is the glow of Christmas morn
That beckons all to the manger where Jesus is born.

About the author

Martha Nelson Phifer was born in Jackson, Louisiana, where her father was a Presbyterian minister. As a pastor's daughter and minister's wife, she has lived in various locations across the South.

She attended Maryville College in Tennessee from 1953 to 1955, but interrupted her studies to be with her husband, Homer, who was attending seminary in Richmond, Virginia. Two decades later, she returned to school and earned a bachelor's degree in literature-communications from the University of North Florida, Jacksonville.

Martha and her husband have one adult son and two grandsons. The Phifers currently live in Harrisonburg, Virginia, where Homer is executive presbyter of Shenandoah Presbytery. Martha is a freelance writer specializing in children's literature and is a member of Trinity Presbyterian Church.

About the illustrator

Judy I. Roberts was born in Philadelphia and grew up in New Jersey. Since childhood, she has had a passion for horses, art, and faith.

Judy set out to study animal science, attending a two-year college in Virginia and Eastern College in St. Davids, Pennsylvania. Eventually, she switched to art and earned a degree from Virginia Commonwealth University in Richmond in 1989.

She and her husband, Richard Hill, live in Harrisonburg, Virginia, where Rick is a Presbyterian campus minister at James Madison University. Judy works as a freelance illustrator and portrait artist. In 1994, she illustrated *Exodus*, a self-published book of her husband's original songs. She also continues to train horses.

Judy is a member of Trinity Presbyterian Church in Harrisonburg, which focuses on mission and service through house churches.

Other picture storybooks from Herald Press:

And It Was Good by Harold Horst Lehman. Colorful artwork illustrates the Creation story from Genesis 1.

April Bluebird by Esther Bender, illustrated by Edna Bender. A brother and sister learn about nature, death, and life.

Are You My Friend? by Janice Derby, illustrated by Joy Dunn Keenan. A boy discovers the many ways people are different from one another—and yet the same.

Let's Make a Garden, written and illustrated by Tamara Awad Lobe. Children from around the world create a garden, using plants, trees, and flowers from their home countries.

The White Feather by Ruth Eitzen, pictures by Allan Eitzen. A story of peacemaking between a white family and Native Americans. Now available in paperback.

Why Are Your Fingers Cold? by Larry McKaughan, illustrated by Joy Dunn Keenan. Delightful answers to questions children ask.

To order these or other Herald Press titles,
call **1 800 759-4447.**